JACK FALLS

Written by PAUL TANTER
Illustrated by OSCAR ALVARADO
Created by PIERS PEREIRA & PAUL TANTER

Soaring Penguin Ltd.
London UK

Jack Falls
Written by PAUL TANTER
Illustrated by OSCAR ALVARADO
Created by PIERS PEREIRA & PAUL TANTER

Produced by Simon Phillips & Toby Meredith
Executive Producers Garry Stewart, Neale Brickwood, Luke Loades, Giles Whitby-Smth, Phil White, Oliver Davies, Mark Davey, Fintan Mcalindon, Steve Lawson, Patricia Rybarczyk and Gillon Stephenson

Published by
Soaring Penguin Ltd.
4 Florence Terrace
Kingston Vale
London
SW15 3RU
www.soaringpenguin.co.uk

First Edition: September 2009

10 9 8 7 6 5 4 3 2 1

ISBN: 9780955287176

Printed in the UK

Chapter one

"Resurrection"

Chapter two

"Reparation"

EVERYONE KNEW CARLY WAS ONE OF THE COMFORTING CONSTANTS IN THEIR LIVES. SHE POURED THE DRINKS AND LISTENED TO THEIR TALES – SOME BULLSHIT, SOME COMPLETELY TRUE BUT SPILLING OUT BECAUSE THEY'D LOST COUNT OF HOW MANY TIMES SHE TOPPED THE GLASS UP.

MORE THAN ANYTHING, SHE WAS NEUTRAL, OR APPEARED TO BE. IT WAS A BIG ASK TO USE HER PLACE. IF PEOPLE FOUND OUT, THEY'D NEVER TRUST HER AGAIN. AND TRUST IS A PRECIOUS COMMODITY THESE DAYS.

I'M OFF IN A MINUTE. REMEMBER TO KEEP THE CURTAINS DRAWN AND THE LIGHTS LOW IF YOU STAY IN.

YES MUM.

THERE'S PLENTY OF FOOD, BUT IF YOU MUST GO OUT, TRY TO BE CAREFUL.

YEAH, I WON'T TALK TO STRANGERS AND LOOK BOTH WAYS BEFORE I CROSS THE ROAD.

I'M GOING TO WORK.

COURSE YOU ARE, YOU GO AND SOAK UP THE SECRETS WHISPERED IN DARK CORNERS. GO AND LOOSEN PEOPLE'S TONGUES BY POURING THEM "JUST ONE MORE DRINK".

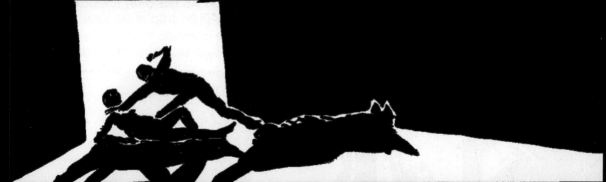

WITH THAT PROBLEM SORTED, I COULD LOOK AT GETTING OUT OF HERE.

THE END